For my beautiful boys, Diego and Pablo, and my beautiful wife, Carla
—J.A.

For the three girls in my life: Amelia, Avery, and my beloved, Darlene
—R.R.

We would like to thank our editor, Mark Siegel, for his invaluable support and enthusiasm for Claudette. We also want to thank the talented crew at First Second: Calista Brill, Colleen AF Venable, and Gina Gagliano. And finally, here are some folks who gave us vital feedback along the way: Carla Gutierrez, Vijaya Iyer, Elizabeth Neal, John Novak, Juan Carlos Perez, Raul Rosado, and Darlene Rosado. Thank you! —Jorge & Rafael

First Second

Published by First Second
First Second is an imprint of Roaring Brook Press, a division of Holtzbrinck Publishing Holdings Limited Partnership
175 Fifth Avenue, New York, New York 10010

Distributed in the United Kingdom by Macmillan Children's Books,
a division of Pan Macmillan.

Cataloging-in-Publication Data is on file at the Library of Congress
ISBN:978-1-59643-582-7

First Second books are available for special promotions and premiums.
For details, contact: Director of Special Markets, Holtzbrinck Publishers.

FIRST
EDITION

First edition 2012
Book design by Colleen AF Venable and Rob Steen
Printed in China by 1010 Printing International Limited, North Point, Hong Kong

20   19   18   17   16   15   14   13   12   11   10

GIANTS BEWARE!

WRITTEN BY
JORGE AGUIRRE

ART BY
RAFAEL ROSADO

STORY BY
RAFAEL ROSADO &
JORGE AGUIRRE

COLOR BY
JOHN NOVAK

ADDITIONAL COLOR BY
MATTHEW SCHENK

:01

First Second
New York & London

"The evil giant would have eaten the toes off of all the babies in Mont Petit Pierre..."
"had it not been for..."
"the brave leadership of..."
"...our great Marquis, Pierre the XXXII."

"Pierre XXXII and his men valiantly chased the giant..."

"all the way up the tallest mountain in the territory."

"And he never bothered our village ever again."

AND THEN WHAT?

5

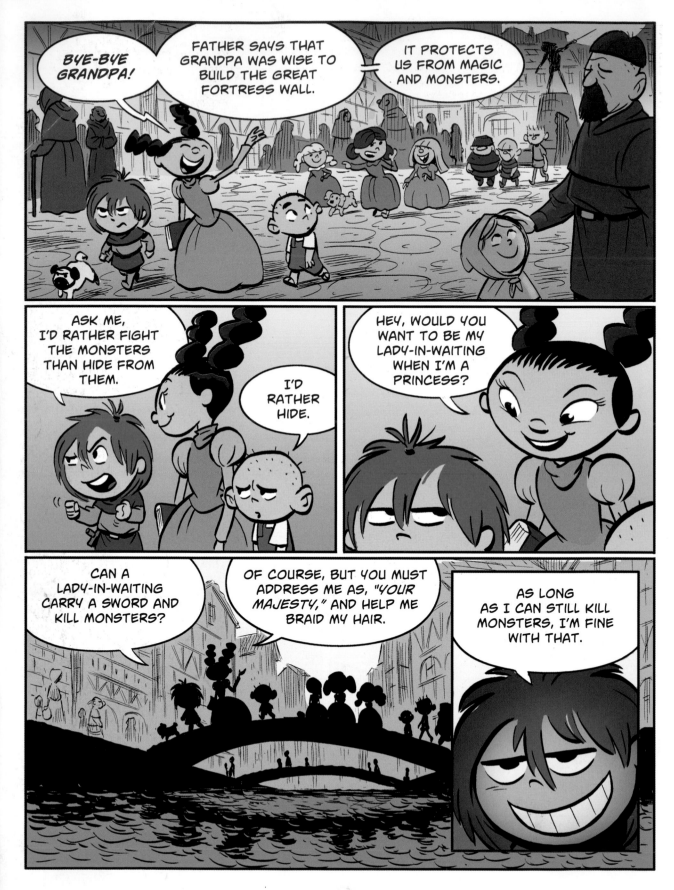

14

15

16

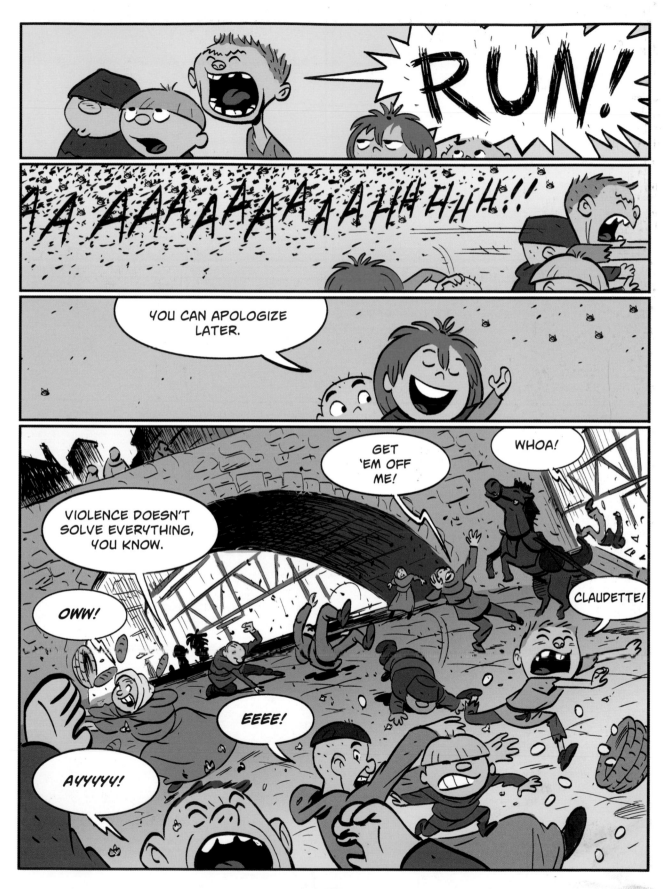

19

31

35

40

43

48

49

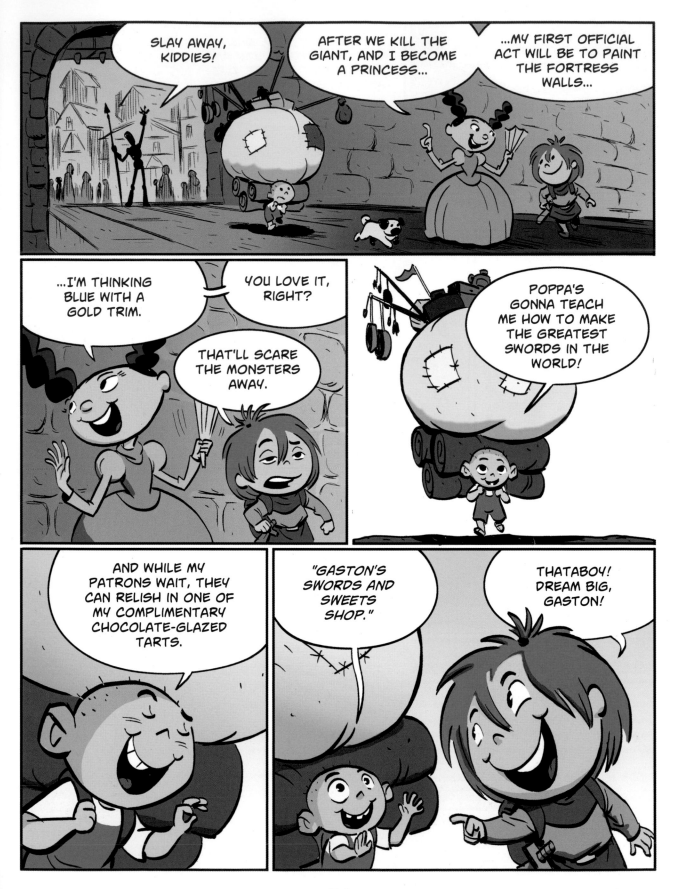

58

60

74

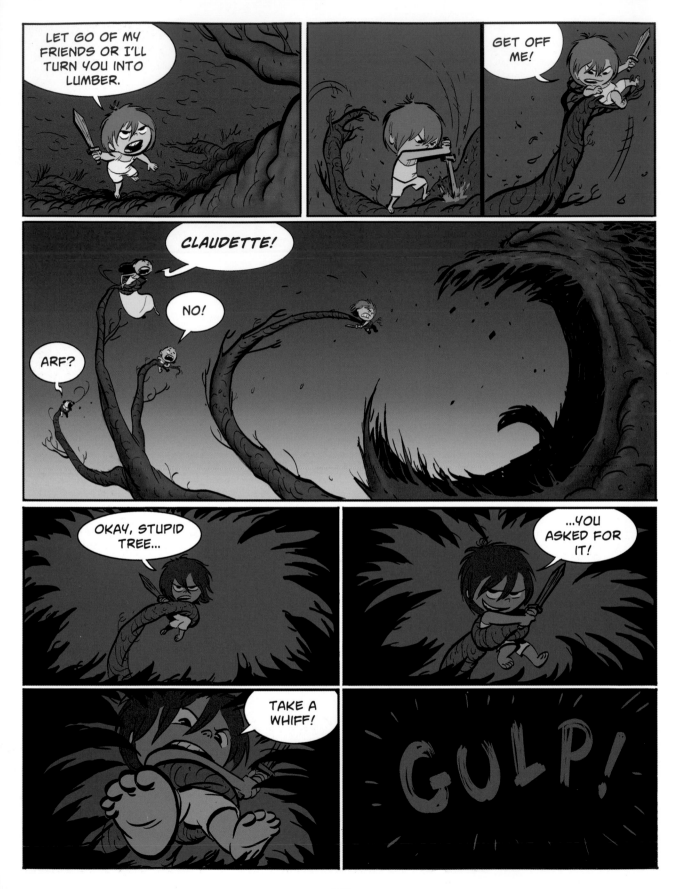

82

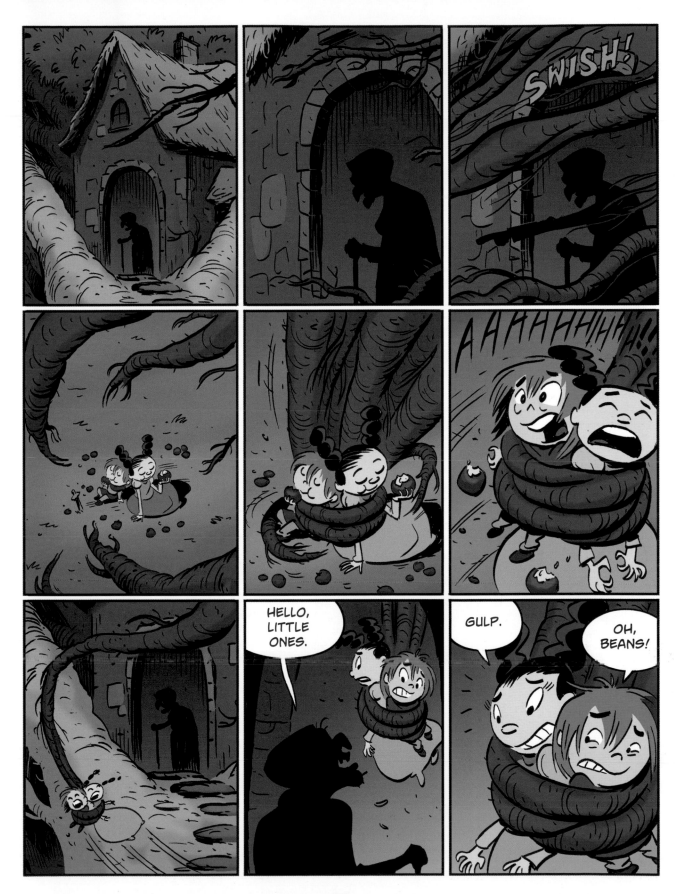

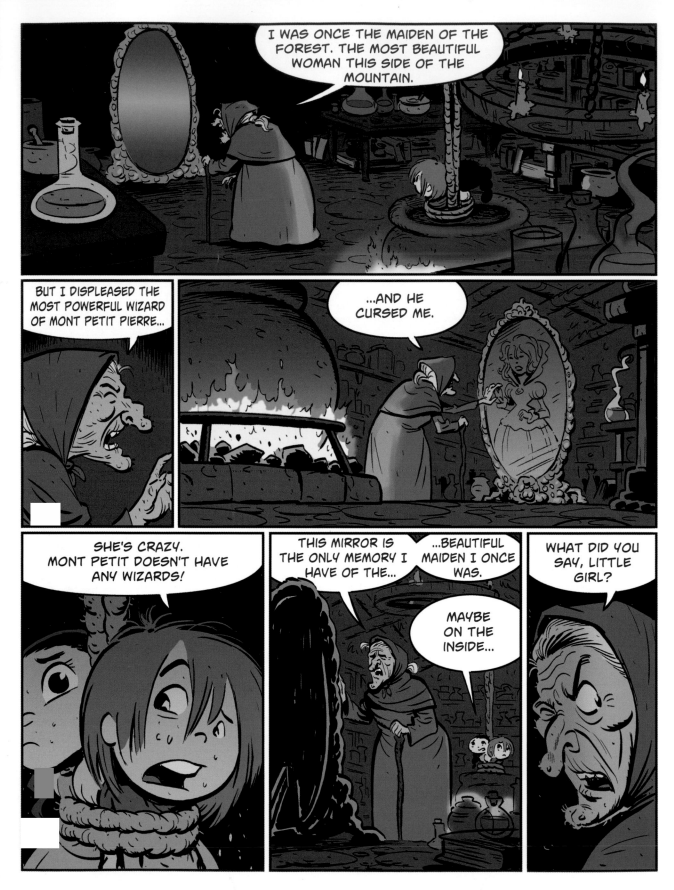

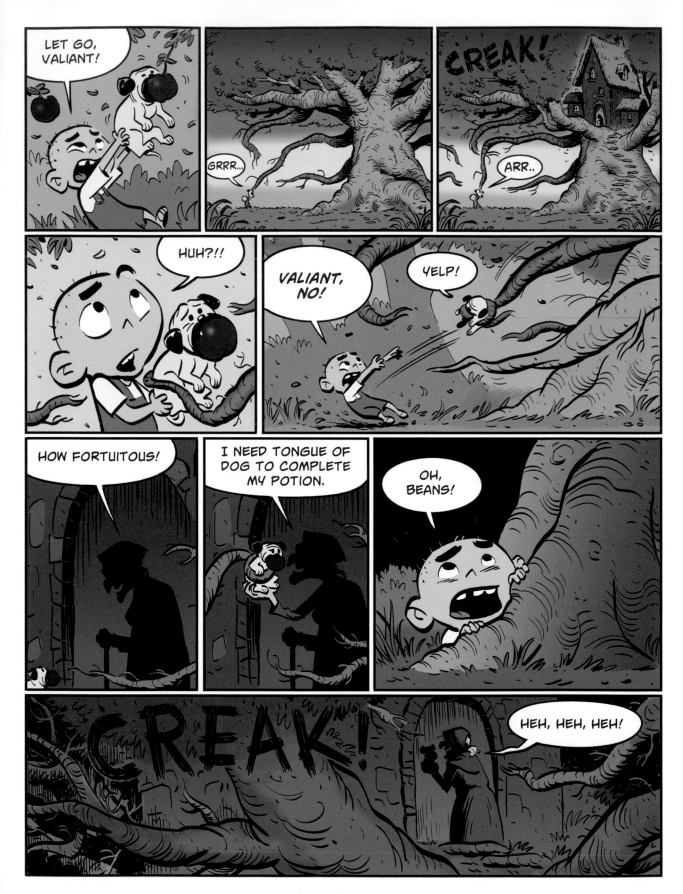

89

91

101

102

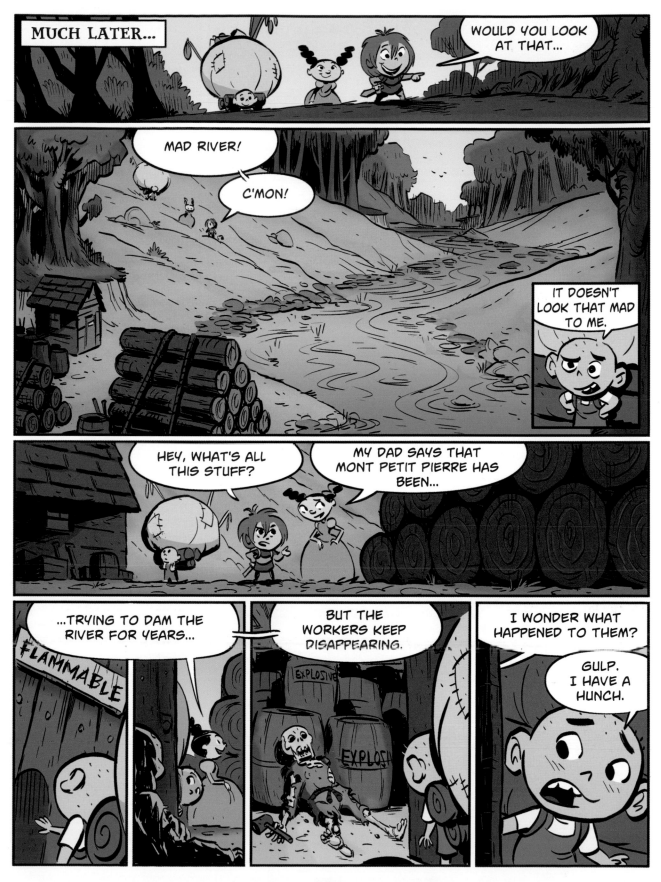

104

114

115

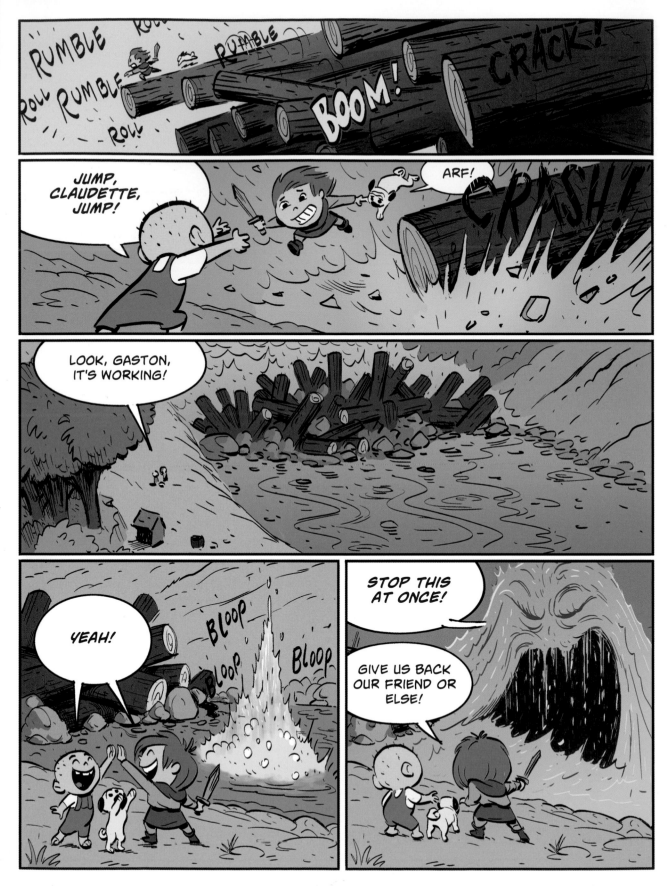

123

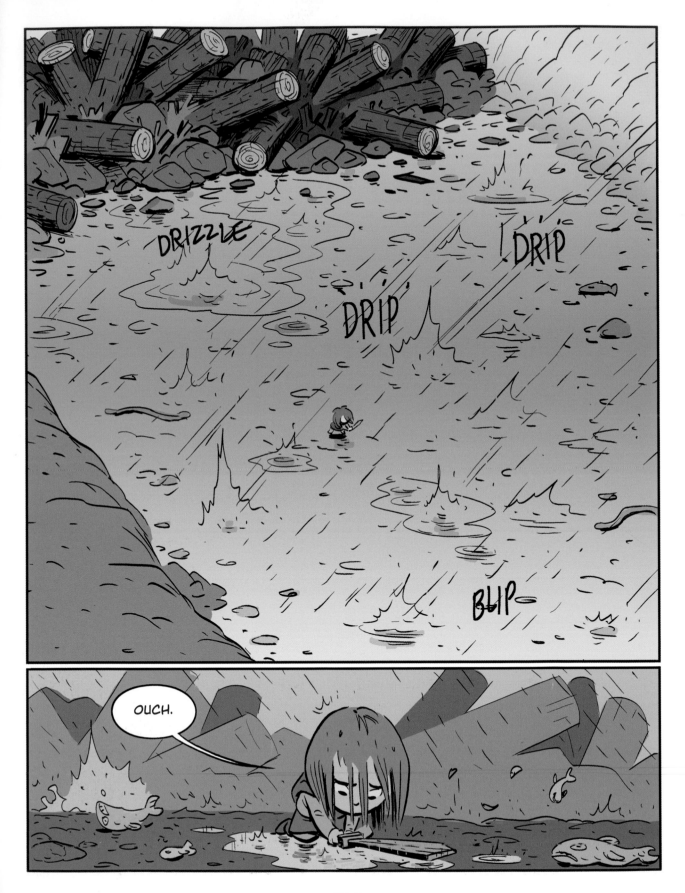

131

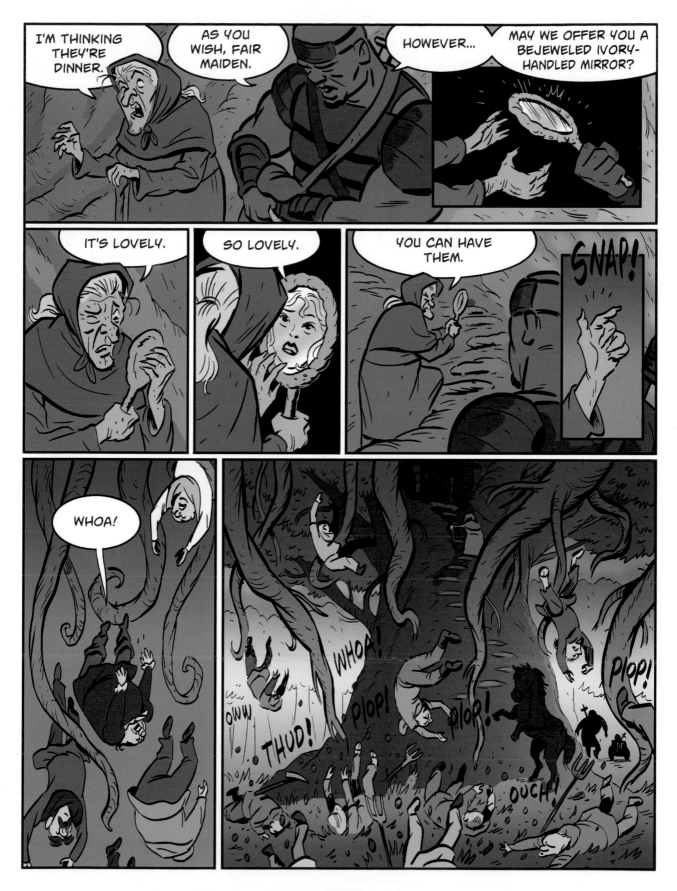

137

139

141

142

143

I CAN'T WAIT TO TELL POPPA HOW I CRUSHED THE APPLE HAG.
I CRUSHED HER, DIDN'T I, CLAUDETTE?
C'MON, PICK UP THE PACE. LOOKS LIKE A BAD STORM'S COMING.
HEY, I'VE BEEN THINKING–
–WHERE ARE ALL THE GIANTS? YEAH, ME, TOO.
DO YOU THINK THE PRINCESS CERTIFICATION BOARD COULD FIND A PROPER PRINCESS FOR THE RIVER KING? THEY MUST GET LOTS OF APPLICANTS.
YOU'D FIGURE GIANTS WOULD BE EASY TO SPOT! THEY'RE GIANT, RIGHT?
DO YOU THINK I SHOULD CONTACT THE BOARD AND ASK THEM?
BABY-FEET-EATING GIANT! SHOW YOURSELF SO I CAN SLAY YOU!
WELL, SHOULD I? SHOULD I ASK THE PRINCESS CERTIFICATION BOARD?
THE WHAT?
IT'S GONNA GET DARK SOON.
CLAUDETTE, WHO EXACTLY SITS ON THE PRINCESS CERTIFICATION BOARD?

146

148

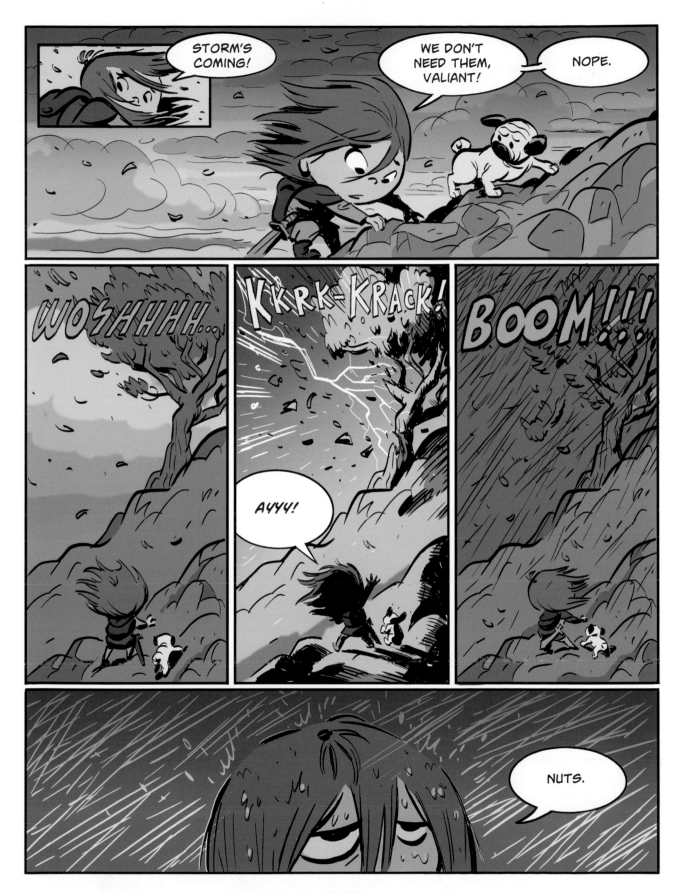

150

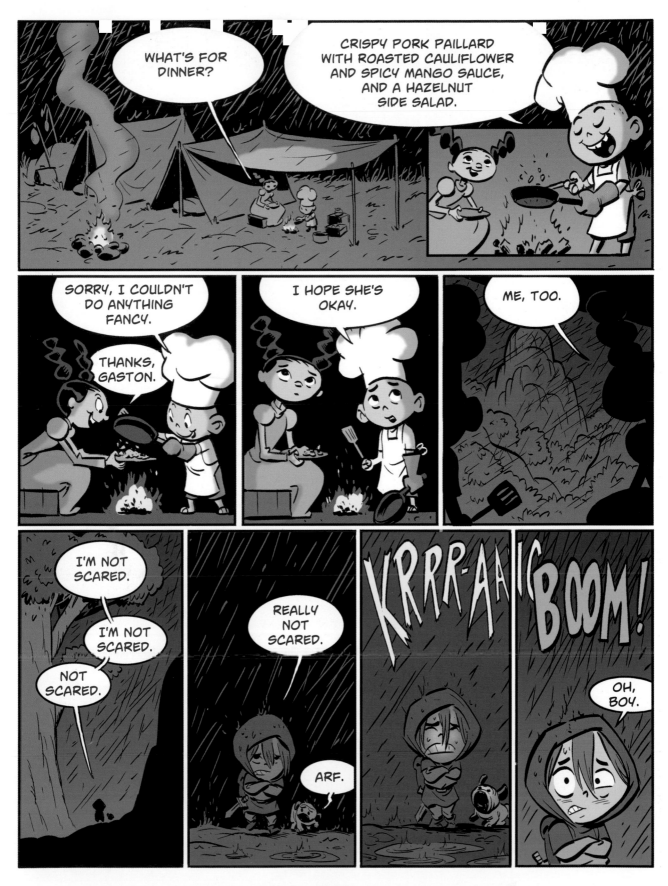

151

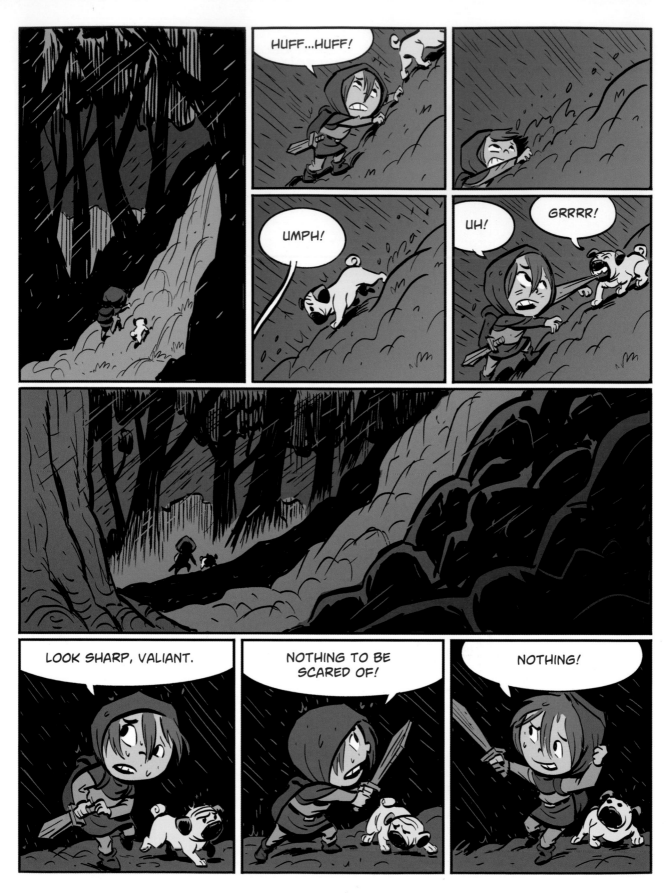

153

155

156

158

163

167

168

169

170

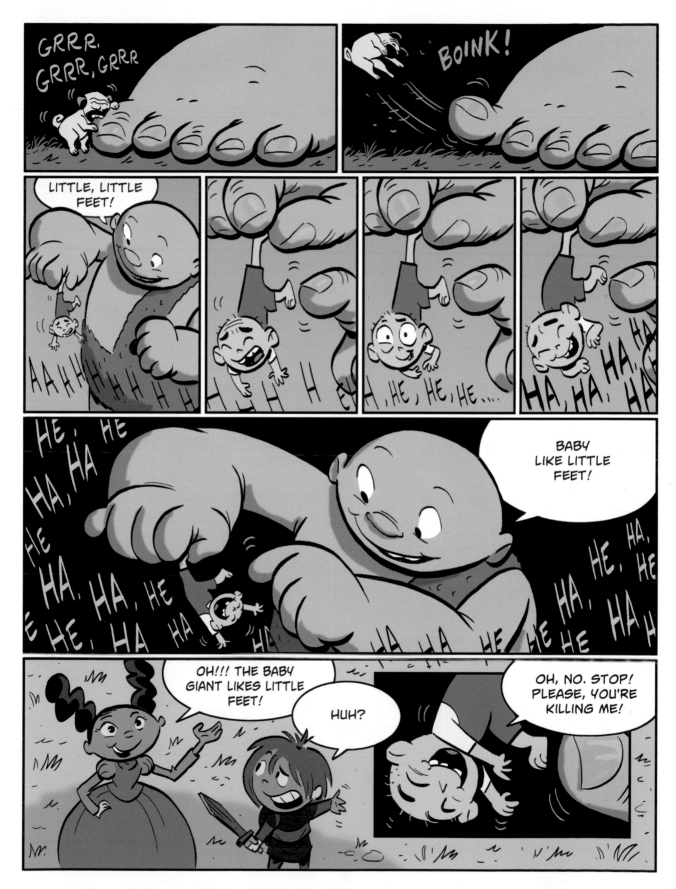

172

173

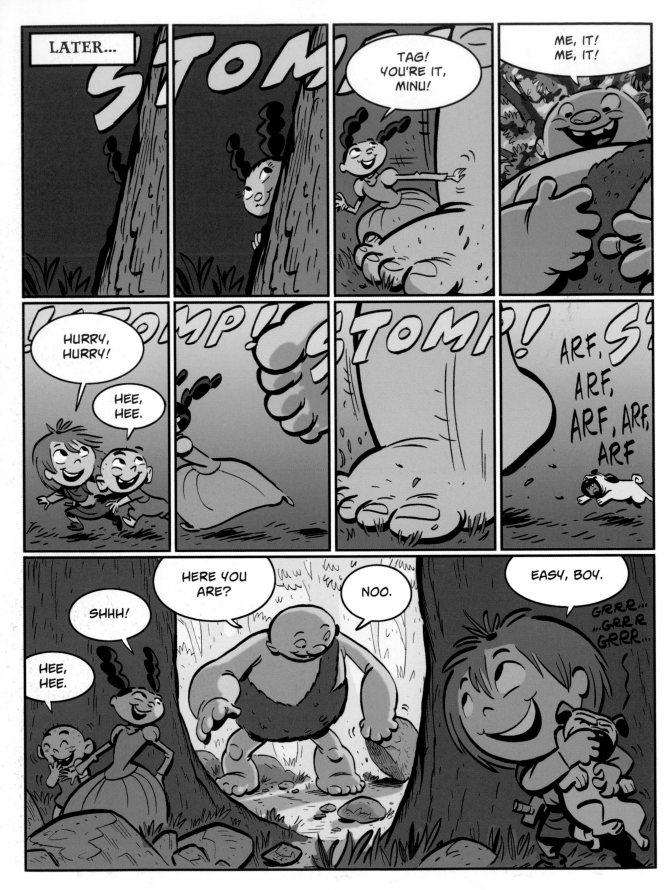

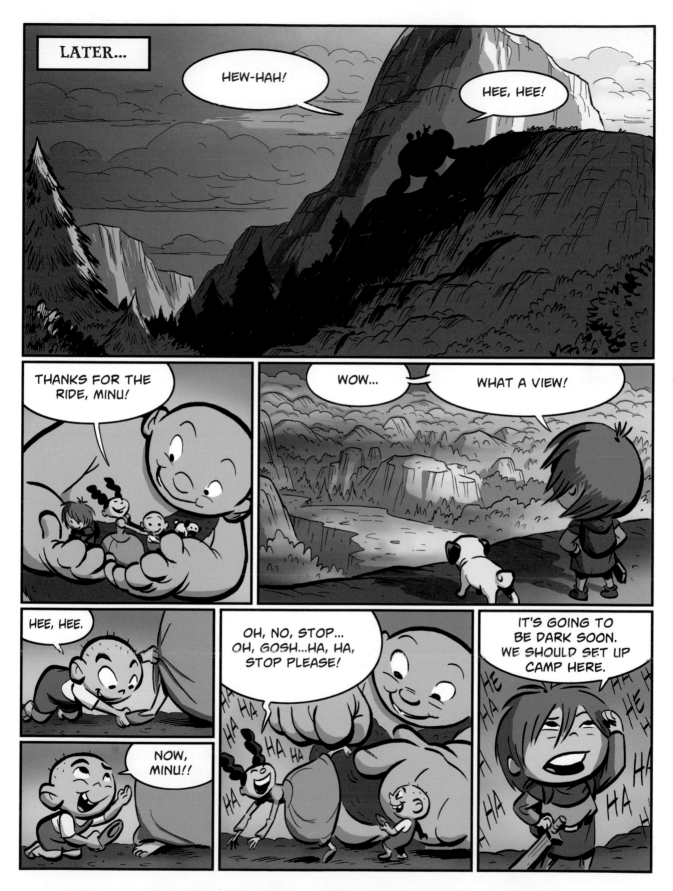

179

181

182

183

185

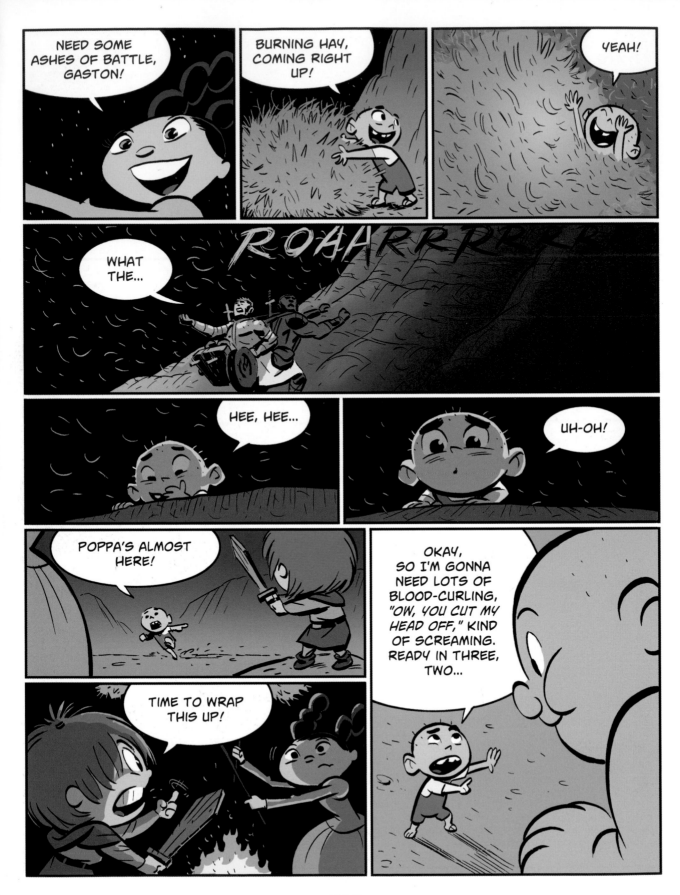

186

189

190

191

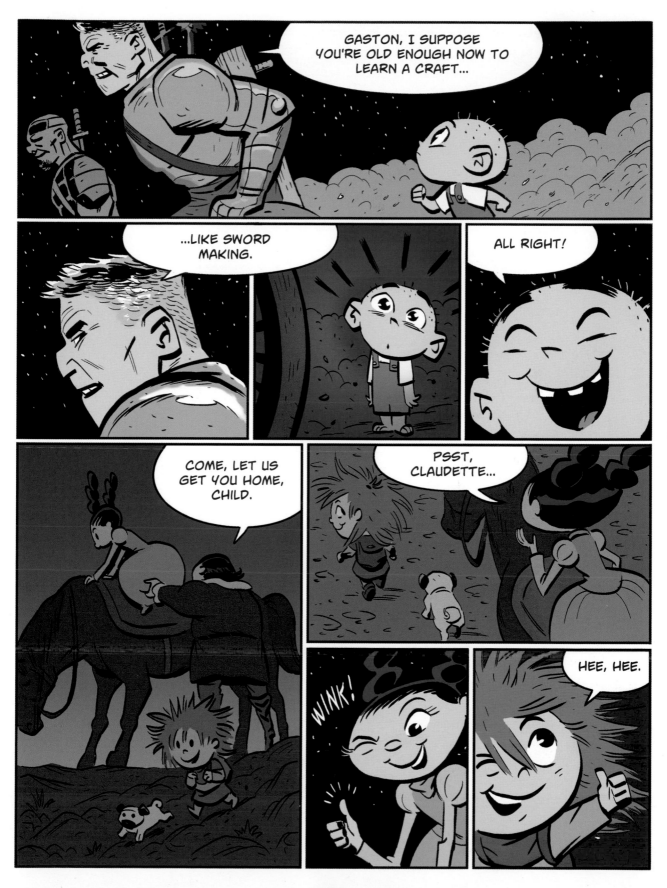

197

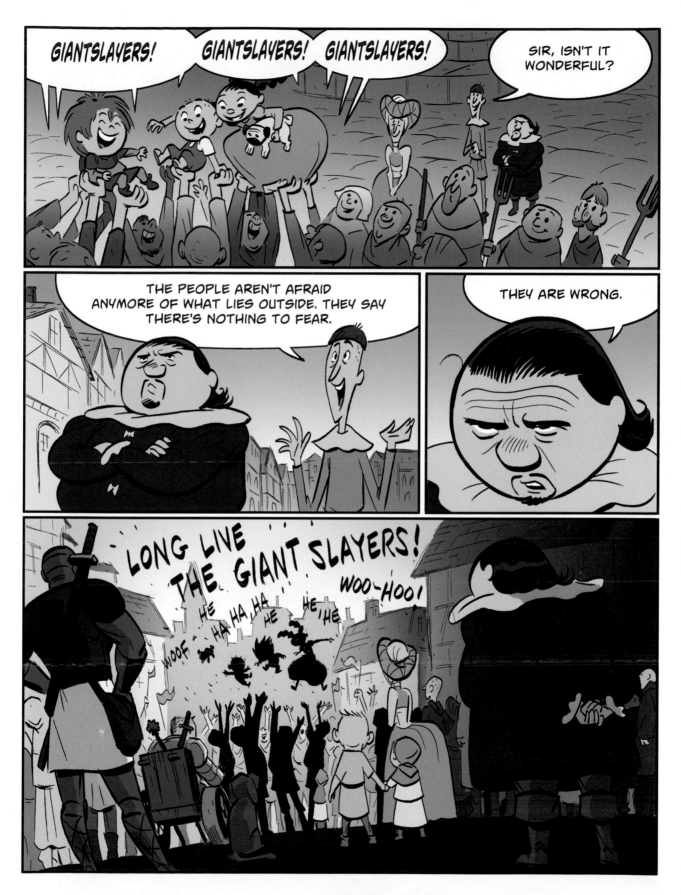

ONE MONTH LATER.